WHaT R U LiKE?

First published in 2005 by
Miles Kelly Publishing Ltd
Bardfield Centre, Great Bardfield
Essex, CM7 4SL

Editorial Director
Belinda Gallagher

Assistant Editor
Hannah Todd

Picture Research
Laura Faulder, Liberty Newton

Designers
Warris Kidwai, Louisa Leitao

Production Manager
Estela Boulton

Scanning and Reprographics
Anthony Cambray, Mike Coupe, Ian Paulyn

British Library Cataloguing-in-Publication Data.
A catalogue record for this book is available from the
British Library

ISBN 1-84236-582-7

Printed in Thailand by Imago

www.mileskelly.net
info@mileskelly.net

WHAT R U LIKE?

Lisa Regan

Miles Kelly

PUBLISHING

Contents

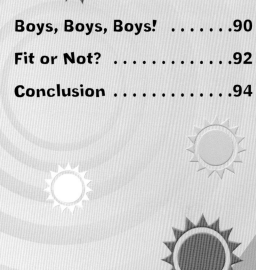

Introduction

What are you like? It's probably been said to you before – but do you know the answer? What are you, your friends and your family, really like? How well do you know them? How much can you tell about other people when you first meet them?

This book is a great way to find out more about yourself and others. It's packed full of quizzes and simple ways to analyse the things you do in everyday life. You'll have great fun answering the questions and following the flow charts to delve deeper into your personality. Your answers will teach you what your responses in certain situations say about you.

You'll also investigate 'subconscious actions' – the things that give away how you're feeling without you even knowing what you're doing. You can learn a lot about people from their handwriting, their hands and the way they move. You don't need to speak to them to find out about them!

What you're really doing as you read this book is starting to explore a science called 'psychology'. That's the study of the mind, looking into why people think and act the way they do.

Nearly 150 years ago, a German scientist called Wilhelm Wundt started doing psychological experiments. He set up a laboratory to study the way people's brains and minds affect their behaviour. Science has come a long way since then...

Cool Science

When psychologists first started studying, the only way to link people's actions to their attitudes was by undertaking behavioural experiments. In the 21st century, psychologists have lots of technology to help them study brains. It's a tricky area though – even if you can see inside a brain, you can't tell what it's actually thinking, or see how the person is feeling.

Like other scientists, psychologists have to come up with theories – their ideas as to why people behave in a certain way. Then they have to carry out experiments to test these theories. They only learn new things by proving or disproving their ideas.

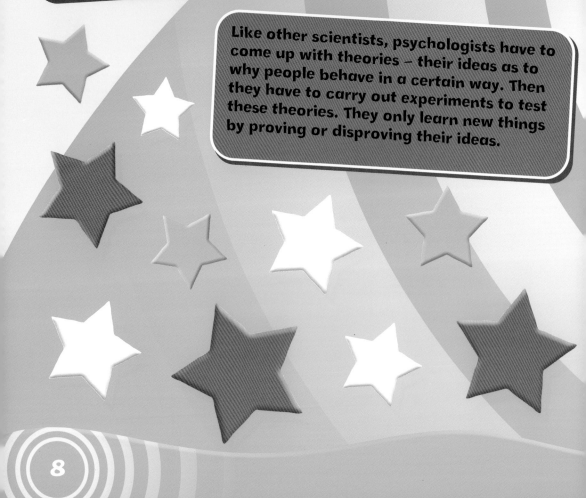

So why do psychologists bother? There are lots of ways in which their work can help today's society. Their studies can help people with behaviour problems, emotional difficulties or damaged brains. That's why psychologists work in many different places – hospitals, schools, offices of large and important companies, prisons, colleges and the government.

If you love studying people – and it's a great way to pass time while you're waiting for a lift, lying on a beach or sitting in a burger bar – then this book is perfect for you. It will give you new things to look for and an idea as to what those things might mean. It will also give you a whole new set of questions for quizzing your friends about their innermost thoughts!

Starter's Orders

Here's a fun and frivolous food quiz to get you started. Grab a pen or pencil and see what your answers reveal about you (turn the page upside down to read the results for each question).

1 Which of these is the yummiest?

Chocolate brownies

Ice cream

Lemon meringue pie

Carrot cake

Chocolate brownies: You're loyal but adventurous, loving new experiences and exciting happenings. You've got a great sense of humour.

Ice cream: You can be selfish and needy, but in contrast to this, you're a great team player. You love sport – watching and joining in.

Lemon meringue pie: You're popular but demanding! You're also a great teacher and good conversationalist.

Carrot cake: You're great fun and have lots of friends. You have a big heart and a quirky sense of humour.

2 Which do you prefer to spread on your toast?

Marmite

Peanut butter

Chocolate spread

Marmalade

Marmite: Ooh! An acquired taste, you love it or hate it. Does that describe you?

Peanut butter: Mix and match with lots of other flavours – do you adapt so easily?

Chocolate spread: What a softy, and oh-so-sweet. Just like you?

Marmalade: Sweet but not sickly – is that how you think of yourself?

3 How do you like your toast?

Dripping in butter

Folded in half

A thin scrape of butter

Hardly brown

Dripping in butter: You live life to the full and love every minute

Folded in half: You have so much to do and so little time!

A thin scrape of butter: Lighten up! You need to enjoy life more

Hardly brown: Don't be afraid to try new things and take a few chances

10

4 What's your favourite snack?

Fruit or nuts

Crisps

Chocolate bar

Biscuits

Fruit or nuts: The healthy option – well done! Stay slim and sporty and you'll have a great life.

Crisps: The savoury option – try to satisfy your hunger with a sandwich or raw veg and hummus instead

Chocolate bar: Uh oh! Make sure this is only a treat every few days, or your teeth and health will suffer

Biscuits: Are you comfort eating? Biccies are okay occasionally but don't eat the whole packet once it's open!

---

5 Which of these do you eat most at the movies?

Popcorn

Tortillas

Pick'n'mix

Chocolate sweets

Popcorn: You like comedy films – it does you good to have a laugh

Tortillas: Your fave films are action movies with lots of noise and fighting!

Pick'n'mix: You love going to see kiddy films – it doesn't matter if your little bro won't go with you!

Chocolate sweets: You're an old romantic and love soppy love stories

---

6 Where would you like to go on a date?

The local chippy

A posh restaurant

A burger bar

A pizza place

Chippy: you're a down-to-earth type who appreciates that it's who you're with that makes a date special, not where you go

Restaurant: Don't be overconfident, or aim too high – pride comes before a fall, remember!

Burger bar: You're not very romantic, are you? Try something new now and then to brighten up your life.

Pizza: You're practical and realistic, but great fun to be with

7 Which of these can you cook best?

Beans on toast

Microwave chips

Curry and rice

Oven-bake pizza

Beans: Well, it's a meal, and you've cooked it – well done! It's not an ambitious project, but at least it's a success.

Microwave chips: Hmm, not exactly Jamie Oliver, are you? You need to learn a few lessons in life before you can look after yourself.

Curry and rice: Well done you! That's a proper meal, and proper cooking. It suggests you're quite mature and responsible generally.

Oven-bake pizza: This shows your practical approach to life – you didn't have to prepare it, but it's a real meal and you're mature enough to use an oven!

8 What's your favourite fruit?

Mango

Banana

Apple

Grapes

Mango: Other people think you're exotic and mysterious, but you're actually very sweet

Banana: You're a sporty type, full of energy and get-up-and-go

Apple: You're down to earth and like to fade into the background

Grapes: You're still a big kid, and just don't want to grow up

9 Which of these drinks do you like best?

Fizzy drinks

Milk

Tea

Water

Fizzy drinks: There's something slightly false about you – are you trying too hard to be popular?

Milk: You're a real home-loving type who's happiest surrounded by family and friends

Tea: You're dying to grow up, and love looking older than you are.

Water: You're super stylish and very trendy. You look good whatever you wear

Is Fame for You?

How would you feel if you were followed by paparazzi and autograph hunters? Here's a fun quiz to see if you're suited to stardom. Choose eight of these that sound most like you:

◇ I like attention, but hate people gossiping about me

✠ Designer clothes are a rip off

✪ I like to do my own thing

◇ I do make people jealous but it doesn't bother me

✠ My house isn't anywhere posh but I love it

✴ I'm not bothered if I do well at school or not

II I can be bossy but I don't do it on purpose

II I'm hyper, even on holiday

✪ I'm quite shy

II If you try hard you'll succeed

✴ I'm very spontaneous and like being the centre of attention

✠ Meeting famous people wouldn't faze me at all

✪ I can go for days without seeing my friends

✴ I LOVE to party!

◇ I don't rely on friends to help me solve my problems

✪ I only have a few close friends

II My temper is quite fiery

✴ I love white witchery, aromatherapy and all that alternative stuff

II Bling is my middle name!

✠ I want a job doing something I love rather than earn millions

✴ I do go through quite a lot of 'new best friends'

Which symbol has the most ticks?

✴ You'd be quite a wild child if you were famous, rebelling against people who want to use your fame and wealth.

◇ Fame would suit you, but only on your terms. If the media try to pry too much, you'll only let them see the bits you want them to see.

✠ You don't want to be famous, although if you get that way by doing something you love, you won't let it change you.

II What a diva! You've invented a 'you' that just has to be famous, no matter how far from the real you it might be.

✪ You crave popularity but are actually very insecure. Being famous would suit one side of your personality but start to destroy the other.

Black Cats and Horseshoes

Does that make you think of lucky charms, or just just roll your eyes at the stupidity of some beliefs? Take this test to find out how superstitious you are.

1

Which of these brings bad luck?

a. Putting your hat on the bed

b. Putting your shoes on the table

c. Putting your dirty fingerprints on the living room wall

2

What do you do when you see the first butterfly of the year?

a. Check its colour – if it's white it means good luck

b. Look for two more – three brings good luck

c. Look at the weather and hope that summer is coming

3

If you see a penny on the floor, what should you do?

a. Leave it alone if it's tails upwards – that's bad luck

b. Pick it up, and all day long you'll have good luck

c. Leave it – it might be stuck down as a practical joke

4

What happens if you knock over the salt and pepper at the table?

a. Aagh! Spilt pepper means a fall out with your best friend

b. Spilt salt brings bad luck unless you throw some over your shoulder

c. You'll have a sneezing fit!

5

Okay, so the pepper makes you sneeze. What should you do?

a. Put your hand over your mouth so your soul doesn't escape

b. Hope someone says 'Bless you'

c. Grab a tissue – it's snot you're catching, not your soul!

6

Which of these would you do if you saw an ambulance go past?

a. Hold your breath until you see a black or brown dog (safe!)

b. Pinch your nose

c. Thank your lucky stars you're not in it

7

Happy birthday to you! It's time for cake – make a wish and...

a. Blow out the candles to make the wish come true

b. Keep it secret or it certainly won't come true

c. Cut the cake so you can scoff it and play more games

8

More wishes – which of these will help your wish come true?

a. Wishing while you're cooking, if you burn the onions

b. Wishing on the first star you see at night

c. Wishing you didn't have to put up with all this rubbish

9

Do you ever 'touch wood'?

a. Yes – three times prevents evil spirits ruining your good fortune

b. Yes – it brings you good luck

c. Yes – if you're playing cricket or climbing trees

10

Your friend wants to show her your 'singing in the rain' routine while you're staying at hers. Do you?

a. No way – putting a brolly over your head indoors is bad luck

b. Nope – it's unlucky to open a brolly in the house

c. Yup – you love fooling around!

How did you score?

Mostly As

Lots of people might think these answers are made up (they're not, though!). You're so superstitious you believe in them all, however extreme they might seem. It's okay to have a couple of things that make you feel secure in life. But don't let them take over your life. And don't hold your breath too long if you see an ambulance!

Mostly Bs

You know many superstitious sayings, and might even stick to some. But you realize that they can affect your life, so only believe in the ones that don't have a big impact. If it makes you feel better, keep wishing and looking out for black cats and horseshoes. We all need a little bit of luck now and then!

Mostly Cs

A load of hocus pocus! You don't believe in much of this stuff, and possibly go out of your way to walk under ladders, step on the cracks in the pavement, and have 13 friends at your party. Carry on doing it your way – but don't be too unkind to people who are more superstitious than you.

Friend or Foe ?

With friends like you, do you soon make enemies?
Or are you the fluffiest friend anyone could wish for?

Start

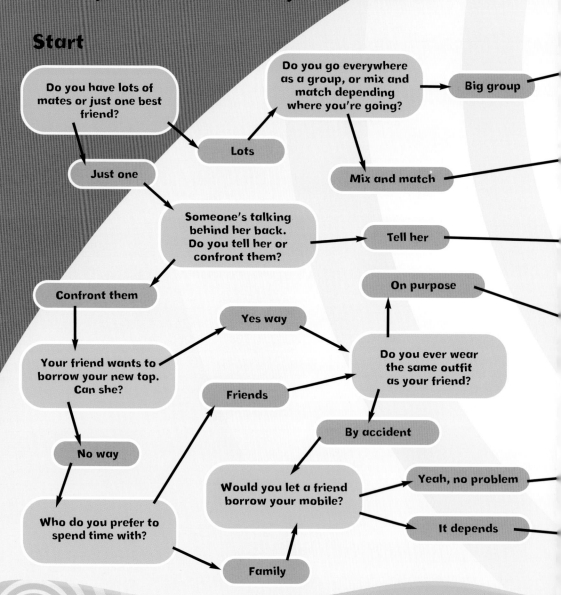

Do you have lots of mates or just one best friend?

Lots

Just one

Do you go everywhere as a group, or mix and match depending where you're going?

Big group

Mix and match

Someone's talking behind her back. Do you tell her or confront them?

Tell her

Confront them

On purpose

Yes way

Your friend wants to borrow your new top. Can she?

Friends

Do you ever wear the same outfit as your friend?

No way

By accident

Would you let a friend borrow your mobile?

Yeah, no problem

It depends

Who do you prefer to spend time with?

Family

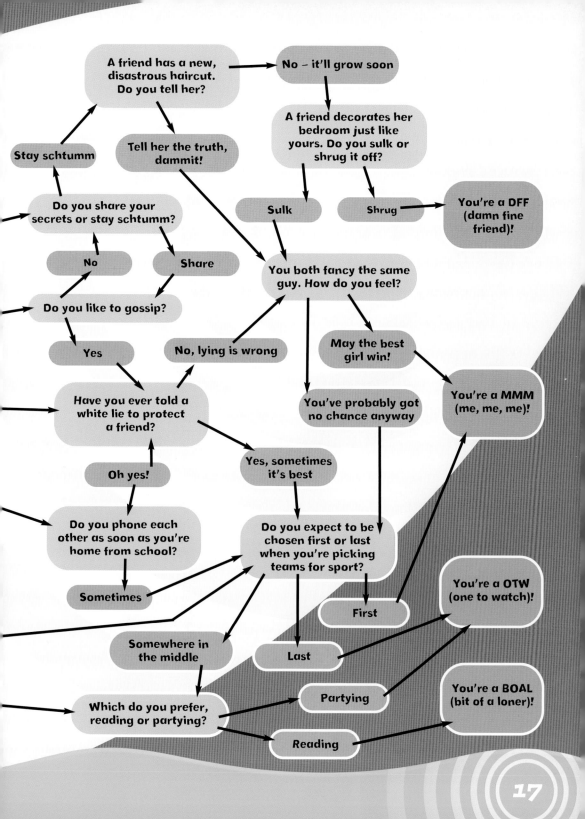

A friend has a new, disastrous haircut. Do you tell her?

No – it'll grow soon

Stay schtumm

Tell her the truth, dammit!

A friend decorates her bedroom just like yours. Do you sulk or shrug it off?

Do you share your secrets or stay schtumm?

Sulk

Shrug

You're a DFF (damn fine friend)!

No

Share

You both fancy the same guy. How do you feel?

Do you like to gossip?

Yes

No, lying is wrong

May the best girl win!

You're a MMM (me, me, me)!

Have you ever told a white lie to protect a friend?

You've probably got no chance anyway

Oh yes!

Yes, sometimes it's best

Do you phone each other as soon as you're home from school?

Do you expect to be chosen first or last when you're picking teams for sport?

You're a OTW (one to watch)!

Sometimes

First

Somewhere in the middle

Last

Partying

You're a BOAL (bit of a loner)!

Which do you prefer, reading or partying?

Reading

Friend or Foe? Results

Which one of these were you?

DFF

You love having lots of friends but are honest, trustworthy and loyal to all of them. Try not to spread yourself too thinly amongst too many people or you'll wear yourself out. You can't please all of the people all of the time – but you're certainly trying hard. Stay the way you are and you'll always have good friends to help you out.

MMM

Ooh, get you, Miss Popular! You love being the centre of a large group of friends. But stop and think – how many of them are true friends who you could rely on in times of need? Having friends isn't just about hanging around in town with lots of people, you know.

OTW

Hmm, you're not too sure what you want from friendship. You haven't got much confidence and your friends don't always know if they can rely on you. Make a start with your one favourite person, and build yourself up to being sociable and dependable with a slightly larger group.

BOAL

You like your own company, but are sensible enough to realize the benefits of having close friends. It's great that you're independent, but make sure your chosen friends know that you're there for them when they need you.

Dream a Little Dream

You might have a good idea of what you're like when you're awake, but what happens when your brain switches to sleep mode? The things you dream about can give clues to thoughts that have been buried during the daytime. Dreams help you 'act out' things that are worrying you, or make decisions that you can't make when you're thinking directly about a problem. If you wake up and remember your dream, write it down straight away. Then you can figure out what the main parts were, to see what's going on in your subconscious mind.

BABY

Welcome to happiness and success, big time! Watch out love-wise, though – someone is trying to seduce you!

BIRTHDAY

Hurray! You're about to enter a trouble-free spell in your life.

Dream a Little Dream II

BREAD

If you're eating it, it's a sign of good health. If you just see it, a risk you take will be successful.

BREATHING

Being out of breath means you're feeling guilty about something you did ages ago.

CAT

A black cat in a dream brings luck. Most other cat dreams, though, are bad news. Your love life could be in trouble, or someone at school is interfering in a negative way.

CHESS

Win or lose? If you won your game, you're having a successful time socially. If you lost, it's a sign you're aiming too high.

CHOCOLATE

You're in a good patch right now – make the most of it.

CHRISTMAS

Good times ahead! Friendship, health and love are all looking good.

DEATH

Don't worry! It's not a bad sign, it just means that you're feeling pessimistic. In fact, dreaming of your own death is sign of good health and good luck on the way.

DOG

Friends are going to help you out – unless the dog is growling, then don't trust them. If the dog bites someone, you're being stubborn over something.

FALLING

A really common thing to dream about, but a sign of loss (of money or love) rather than anything really scary.

FIGHTING

Dreaming you're in a fight isn't good, especially if you're in love or going on a journey. Watch out for enemies.

Dream a Little Dream III

FOUNTAIN

A great sign (showing health, wealth and good fortune), but if the water is dirty, this shows bitterness and trouble.

HIDING

Loosen up a bit – you're crowding someone out or being too hard upon yourself.

MONSTER

As you'd expect, it's really not a good thing to dream about. You may be feeling a little bit depressed – try to focus on the reasons why and change them for the better to get rid of the monsters in your dreams.

MOON

A sign of hope and harmony and good for your love life.

SHEEP

Yay! A sign of good fortune, unless they're running away from you, in which case you're feeling picked on.

NAKEDNESS

It's common to dream that you're naked, but not good. You need to get help with you're emotional problems.

SNAKES

Watch out! Someone's trying to ruin your love life or your money matters.

STORM

Be careful! There may be dangers ahead, so lean on others for help if you need it.

SWAN

A good sign – luck, love or money is coming your way.

TEETH

Mostly a bad sign, although if you're having a filling, good things are ahead.

THROWING

You're feeling dissatisfied at the moment – take time to find out why and try to resolve things.

TREES

Climbing trees, or seeing trees full of leaves or fruit, are great signs for the future. A tree in a storm represents family problems, and one being cut down signifies the loss of a friendship.

Inny or an Outy?

Not a quiz about your belly button, but a quick test to see if you're introverted or extroverted. Tick your answers then turn the page to find out more about yourself.

1 How many close friends do you have?
a. Just one best friend ☐
b. Two or three best friends ☑
c. Lots of good friends ☐

2 You've got some major news. What do you do?
a. Keep it to yourself for a day while you get used to it ☐
b. Text your friends to tell them ☑
c. Phone everyone you know ☐

3 When you're with your friends, what's the conversation like?
a. You love listening to what's being said ☑
b. You like to join in with your own news ☐
c. You always talk first and are full of fun ☐

4 When you talk, which of these happens most?
a. You take time to think about what you're going to say ☑
b. You sometimes feel you've said the wrong thing ☐
c. You talk first and think afterwards ☐

5 Could you spend a day without emailing, phoning, texting, or talking to anyone else?
a. You wouldn't mind ☐
b. It would be interesting to see if you could do it ☐
c. No way! You'd go bonkers ☑

6 What do you do at weekends?
a. Shop with your mates ☐
b. Get together with friends but also catch up on stuff you need to do at home ☐
c. Kick around the house, reading, chilling, or doing fave hobbies ☑

7 What do you do when you walk into a party?
a. Find a group of people to talk to ☐
b. Look for someone you know ☑
c. Wait to see what kind of party it is, and if anyone looks friendly ☐

8 What do you do if you know the answer to a teacher's question?
a. Stick your hand up in the air ☑
b. Wonder about the answer ☐
c. Hope the teacher doesn't make you speak out loud ☐

9 How do you shop?

a. You look in all the shops and go back to those you want to buy from ☑

b. You often don't buy things as you can't face walking from one end of town to another to get them ☐

c. Make a list of what you need ☐

10 Which of these do you hear most from your parents?

a. You've already told me that a thousand times ☐

b. Why do you only tell us half of the things happening in your life? ☐

c. You never told me that! ☑

11 Are you a touchy-feely person?

a. I guess I hug my close family ☐

b. I hug people to say hello or thank you ☐

c. Yeah, me and my friends are always hugging and linking arms ☑

12 What happens when you have a great idea?

a. You think long and hard until it's worked out, then tell a few people ☐

b. You write it down then show people ☐

c. You talk about it, getting louder and more excited as the idea forms ☑

13 Which of these best describes you?

a. Quite laid back about the way you approach things ☐

b. Sometimes nervous but not always ☐

c. Always in a rush to try things ☑

14 How would you describe yourself?

a. Someone who doesn't miss much about other people ☐

b. Quite good at listening to others ☐

c. A chatty, lively type of person ☑

15 If you're queuing and someone talks to you, how do you feel?

a. I'd rather just wait in line quietly ☐

b. I don't mind people talking to me unless I'm having a bad day ☐

c. I'll happily chat to waste a bit of time ☑

16 Do you judge people on your first impressions?

a. Yes, I'm a good judge of character ☐

b. Sometimes, but I like to know what other people think too ☐

c. No, I prefer to get to know them first ☑

17 Do you get bogged down by deadlines?

a. No, I just plan ahead ☐

b. No, I work better under a bit of pressure ☐

c. Yes, I'd rather do things at my own pace ☑

18 How would you (not your parents!) describe your bedroom?

a. It's tidy and I know where everything is ☐

b. It's not bad for someone my age! ☐

c. It's a bit messy but I'm too busy to tidy up ☑

19 Which of these best describes your wardrobe?

a. Full of clothes I wear all the time ☑

b. *Random* – lots of clothes don't match ☐

c. Full of bargains that I wish I'd never bought ☐

20 What sort of films do you like?

a. Romances and films based on books ☐

b. All sorts – kids' movies, historical films, thrillers ☑

c. Action packed adventures with hunky heroes ☐

Inny or an Outy? Results

Questions 1–5 a = 1 b = 2 c = 3   Questions 11–15 a = 1 b = 2 c = 3
Questions 6–10 a = 3 b = 2 c = 1   Questions 16–20 a = 3 b = 2 c = 1

20–40

You've definitely got an introverted side to you. Don't worry, it's not a bad thing! It simply means that you act differently to a more extroverted person, not worse or better. The higher your score, the more you're heading towards a balance of introvert/extrovert.

You like your own company and are happy to spend time alone or not talking all the time. That doesn't mean you don't have good friends, though – just that you don't need to be with them constantly. Your personality actually makes you a great friend – you're loyal and a really good listener.

You prefer to think and plan before you act and quite often you do the same in conversation. That means you come across as quiet, but when you do say something, people know it's worth listening to.

The main downside to being an introvert is that you might get a bit shy when you have to meet new people. Don't panic – remember that you don't have to be the loudest person in the room for people to want to get to know you.

41–60

You're much more of an extrovert (although the lower your score, the more you have a quieter side). You like to surround yourself with people and need constant conversation to keep you buzzing. Sometimes you can't even think without saying it out loud!

You're great at talking through problems and coming up with ideas quickly. You've probably already noticed at school that you work best in a group session when you can all fling ideas around. You're going to be a great team leader one day!

Parties are a great way to socialize and you get a real buzz from meeting new people. However, you have to realize that not all people are as lively as you. You might make friends or get together with boys who wish you would keep quiet sometimes. Often they find your chatter annoying, or even worse, feel that you're nagging or droning on. Try to take time to be on your own and let others have the space they need.

Number Crunching

The day you were born has a big part to play in the way you live your life and the kind of person you turn out to be. As well as deciding which star sign you are (if you believe in astrology and horoscopes), your birthday also gives you certain 'personality numbers' that show your best characteristics – and your worst!

To find out your personality number, you have to do some maths. First, write down your date of birth in full:

15 July 1993

Now change the month to a number, depending on its place in the year (so January = 1, February = 2 and so on):

15/7/1993

Next, add every single number together in a big sum:
$$1 + 5 + 7 + 1 + 9 + 9 + 3 = 35$$

Finally, add the figures of this answer together until you get a single number:
$$3 + 5 = 8$$

If your number is still two figures (eg 48: $4 + 8 = 12$) add them again to get a single number ($1 + 2 = 3$).

All done? Now use your personality number to find out your inborn characteristics, favourites and talents.

NUMBER	Good Points	Bad Points
1	Clever, brave, independent, organized, good leader	Over-sensitive, selfish, stubborn, bossy
2	Friendly, sympathetic, reliable, patient, quiet	Shy, lifeless, lacking ambition or energy
3	Outgoing, lively, interesting, happy, popular, talented	Big-headed, show-off, bossy, wasteful, critical
4	Hard working, trustworthy, loyal, practical, logical	Stubborn, argumentative boring, jealous, stingy
5	Enthusiastic, intelligent, dramatic, free-spirited, creative, inventive	Moody, sarcastic, greedy, unreliable, temperamental, vain, wasteful
6	Intelligent, home-loving, considerate, peacemaking, charming, loyal	Extravagant, picky, wasteful, selfish, vain, underhanded, nagging
7	Thoughtful, intelligent, sympathetic, artistic, inventive, spiritual	Withdrawn, lonely, shy, critical, stand-offish, moody
8	Ambitious, helpful, brave, wise, successful, sincere, reliable	Bossy, greedy, big-headed, power-crazy
9	Adventurous, exciting, interesting, loving, generous, creative	Wasteful, self-pitying, lonely, over-emotional, not bothered

And there's more!
Turn the page to work out your 'name number'
and find out what that says about you, too!

What's Your Name Number?

First, write down your full name. Use the table below to find the number value for each of the letters and write those underneath. For example:

CHRISTINA   MARIA   AGUILERA
3 8 9 9 1 2 9 5 1   4 1 9 9 1   1 7 3 9 3 5 9 1

Add them all together in a big sum, like you did for your birthday:
$3 + 8 + 9 + 9 + 1 + 2 + 9 + 5 + 1 + 4 + 1 + 9 + 9 + 1 + 1 + 7 + 3 + 9 + 3 + 5 + 9 + 1 = 109$

Add these numbers again until you get a single figure:
$1 + 0 + 9 = 10$
$1 + 0 = 1$

Now you can look up your personality type opposite! Don't forget to try it for your friends' names, or any classmates you secretly fancy!

NUMBER VALUES

1	2	3	4	5	6	7	8	9
A	B	C	D	E	F	G	H	I
J	K	L	M	N	O	P	Q	R
S	T	U	V	W	X	Y	Z	

1173 89615

1 You're a true leader – brave, original, good at solving problems and full of energy. Be careful not to be too bossy or selfish, though.

2 You're great at seeing both sides of an argument, so you make a good peacemaker. You're tactful with a good sense of humour, and love meeting new people.

3 You make a fab friend as you're sympathetic, generous and love to help. Don't forget to be nice to yourself sometimes!

4 Steady as a rock, you are! Determined and honest, you work hard for what you want.

5 A free spirit, you love travelling to see new things, meeting people and learning as much as you can. Beware of being loudmouthed and possessive.

6 You'd make a great teacher because you love passing on knowledge and advice. Watch out for emotional highs and lows.

7 A perfectionist! And a bit of a loner, too – not very good at relying on other people in case they don't live up to your expectations.

8 Three important words in your life: money, success, power. You could be the next Bill Gates or Prime Minister!

9 Love – your life is full of it, and you extend it to friends, family and the world in general. You're looking for fame, not fortune.

Time and Tide

Are you summer lovin' or do you prefer a winter wonderland? Tick all the statements that you agree with and add up your score at the end.

- ☑ I'm quite a sporty person
- ☐ I have to have an alarm clock to wake up on time
- ☐ All of my winter clothes are bright colours
- ☐ Snowball fights are fun!
- ☐ People say I'm the life and soul of a party
- ☐ Going to sleep is usually easy
- ☐ I'm at my best in the mornings
- ☐ I start my Christmas shopping in the January sales!
- ☐ Sometimes I feel low but can't figure out why
- ☐ I buy loads of CDs and DVDs
- ☐ Picnics are so cool!
- ☐ Surfing is for showoffs
- ☐ Slobbing in front of the telly isn't my style
- ☐ I get my calcium from hot chocolate with extra cream!
- ☐ I'd love to be a surf chick
- ☐ I watch at least two soaps regularly
- ☐ If at first you don't succeed, try again!

- I love my family to bits
- Kids' ice cream is cooler than Haagen-Dazs
- I'm often more attracted to a guy's personality than his looks
- I wear bikinis instead of underwear in the summer
- Barbecue food does my head in – burnt on the outside, raw on the inside!
- I love flirting
- I'm usually in a good mood
- I always seem to be busy
- I hate getting my hair wet when I'm swimming
- I find it hard to relax and get to sleep at night
- I'm a perfectionist
- I'd love to travel to Australia or India
- I've never seen the sun rise!
- I love buying new clothes
- My brolly is so cool and funky!
- I get bored really easily
- I prefer team sports as it's easier to be motivated
- I'd love to go to a music festival
- I love snuggling up with my boyfriend
- Skiing looks fun but cold
- Cats are one of my fave animals
- I've taken some really cool photos of sunsets
- I wear black clothes a lot

Time and Tide Results

Now go back and see what you've ticked. Start with a score of 200 and take off ten points for every blue statement you've ticked. Add on ten points for every red statement you've ticked. What does it tell you about yourself?

0–140

You're a sunny, summer person! You're outgoing and full of life, and when the Sun's out it gives you a real energy boost that makes you want to try new things and meet new people. You tackle new projects with enthusiasm and love getting others to join in. Just remember that not everyone is the same as you, so be gentle with people who are nervous of trying new things.

160–240

You're an inbetweeny! You probably love the best bits of autumn and spring, which means that you're always open to change. You're happy to follow someone else's lead but won't do anything you don't want to do. Your style is your own and you're going to stick to it!

260–400

You love winter, but that doesn't mean you're cold-hearted. Far from it! You love snuggling up and getting cosy, although you're very happy in your own company. Don't use nasty weather as an excuse for not socializing – wrap up warm and brave the outdoor world with your best mates.

Left-brained or Right-brained?

Yup, just like being left- or right-handed, scientists think that people are ruled more by one side of their brain than the other. Read this long list and circle the entries that you think apply to you.

Logical	Sensuous	Good with facts	Creative
Analytic	Imaginative	Likes maths/numbers	Visual
Good with words	Technological	Remembers song words	Remembers song tune
Critical	Abstract	Sees fine detail	Good with ideas
Thoughtful	Impulsive	Practical	Imaginative
Intellectual	Free	Right-handed	Mystical
Realistic	Timeless	Keeps things in order	Quiet
Outspoken	Artistic	Rational	Left-handed

If your circles were in the first and third columns, you're governed by your left brain. You're likely to enjoy things that use logical thought such as map reading, plans and diagrams. When you start work, you should do well in a business environment and you're probably organized and good with people. If you circled more in the second and fourth columns, you're more of a right-brained, 'artistic' person – good at thinking creatively and seeing things that other people don't. You'd be good at teaching or helping others. You'll enjoy 'spiritual' things such as palm-reading, yoga or listening to music.

This little puzzle helps show the difference between the two sides of your brain. Read the list but say out loud the COLOUR of the writing, not the word you're reading. Your right brain tries to say the colour but your left brain wants to read the word.

Yellow Blue Orange
Black Red Green
Purple Yellow Red
Orange Green Black
Blue Red Purple
Green Blue Orange

Body Language

Can you tell when someone's lying to you? If you're bored during a conversation, can other people tell? It's great to be able to decipher what other people are thinking, just by studying the signs their bodies give away.

Big fibbers

Lots of people don't make eye contact while they're talking as it makes them uncomfortable in a conversation. However, if someone has been meeting your eye while they're talking, and then looks downwards or sideways, the chances are they're not telling the truth at that moment.

Little fibbers

Little brothers and sisters are the best people to watch when they're trying to fib, as they haven't learnt how to cover up their guilty signs. If they're fidgeting, squirming and looking at the floor, you can bet they're up to no good!

The cover up!

Watch out also for someone coughing over a sentence. Unless they've already shown signs of germs, a single cough (with their hand over their mouth) is often a sign that they're trying to 'cover up' something untrue.

Loves me, loves me not

How can you tell if someone fancies you if they don't tell you? Eye contact, again, is a good sign as it shows they're interested in what you're saying. Tilting their head to one side is also an indication. Lots of girls flick their hair with their hands to show a guy they're interested – do you do this? Without knowing it, lots of people flare their nostrils or pout their lips if they're attracted to someone. Weird but true!

Mini-blushes

You may blush when you feel embarrassed but watch out for 'mini-blushes' if you're with a person you like. Their cheeks might get red, showing they like you, or it could just affect the tips of their ears. They may get sweaty palms, too, so check to see if they rub their hands together a lot!

Body Language II

Okay, so you're not on the lookout for a fibber or a boyfriend – what can other body language tell you?

Adam's apple

This is the lump in a man's throat. If it jumps unexpectedly, it may mean they're nervous.

Hands

Is the person you're watching using their hands in conversation? Are they always palms up or palms down? Palms up shows they're friendly and approachable. Palms down is more a sign that they're feeling aggressive or very confident about what they're saying. If they join their fingertips like a church steeple, they're thinking hard and listening carefully.

Crossed arms

Often just a comfortable way to place your arms, but if they're too tightly folded it shows the person is feeling defensive.

Eyebrows

People often lower their eyebrows in a scowl but it might not be a sign of grumpiness. It could mean the person disagrees with what's just been said, or wants to question it. Raised eyebrows with a smile shows they really find something funny, but can show surprise or disbelief.

Lips

Clenched lips (held together tightly) can show that someone is getting angry, or doesn't like what's being said. It can show sadness, too, so be careful what you say! Pursed lips, like the start of a kiss, shows the person doesn't agree with you, or is scheming about something.

Sleep Tight

Body language doesn't just work in conversation. It's such a subconscious thing that scientists even think it can take over our sleeping bodies. Read the descriptions on this page. Which one do you think is most like the way you sleep?

1 Foetus (curled up)

This is the most common way to sleep. It shows that you can be defensive but you're a softy at heart. You may be a bit shy when you first meet people, but on the whole you're friendly and easy to get on with.

② Log (super straight)

You're easy to get to know, and love being in the middle of a crowd. You have lots of friends, and enjoy socializing with new people. Be careful not to welcome new people too quickly – take time to get to know them, as not everyone is as nice as you.

③ Yearner (reaching out)

You also like meeting people but are more wary and untrusting. You don't judge on first impressions. Whatever decisions you make in life, you think about them long and hard. Once you've made your mind up, though, you stick to a decision.

Sleep Tight II

1 ## Soldier (standing up)

You sleep as if you've literally fallen asleep on your feet! That's typical of you – no fuss, no complaining, you would sleep wherever you were put! Although you're quiet and keep your thoughts to yourself, you're quite a perfectionist and often feel other people don't meet your high standards.

2 ## Freefaller (face down)

Do you cuddle your pillow as you sleep? It's a sign that you don't like to be criticised and often find new situations scary. You sometimes hide your nerves by being loud and trying to be the centre of attention.

3 ## Starfish (flat out)

You're a really good friend and a great listener. You'd rather others were in the spotlight as you don't like to be noticed so much. You'll lend a helping hand whenever you can.

Super-shallow fragilistic!

Answer true or false to the statements below.

	True	False		True	False
I wouldn't go out with someone more than a year younger than me	☐	☐	I've totally fallen for cute guys I've seen around town	☐	☐
All of my friends are really pretty	☐	☐	If I'm talking to someone nerdy, I keep looking for an escape route	☐	☐
I spend lots of money on designer clothes	☐	☐	I laugh at jokes even if I don't understand them	☐	☐
I don't like talking to people with lots of spots	☐	☐	I have a new best friend every month or so	☐	☐
I'd love to go out with someone older than me	☐	☐	I've done stuff I hate just to impress my new boyfriend	☐	☐
I wear make-up all the time	☐	☐	I do bitch about my friends behind their back if they bug me	☐	☐
Expensive clothes are sooooo much better than cheap fashion items	☐	☐			
I always phone my friends to gossip after school	☐	☐	Geeks should stick together and not try to be popular	☐	☐

How many did you tick 'True' for? Just a couple is okay – lots of people judge a book by its cover every now and then. If you ticked more than six, you really need to change your values. The world doesn't have to be full of beautiful people to be a beautiful place, you know. Learn to look under the surface of things – you're just too shallow!

Doodle Dandy

Do you doodle? Check your school books or the notepad by the telephone – are they covered in squirls, squares and colouring in? Sometimes it's just a sign of boredom (especially shading in the middles of letters). However, the things you doodle when you're not really concentrating can tell you more about yourself.

Noughts and crosses

If you play little games with yourself, or draw other game-related shapes like a chess board or football pitch, it's a sign that you're competitive in everything you do.

Random shapes

If it looks like your pen has taken over your hand, it shows that you're not good at concentrating and your mind is totally on something else. It's quite often a sign of being tense or stressed.

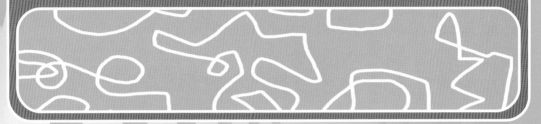

Stars and moons

This can mean that your head is in the heavens – lack of concentration again. Or it could mean you're very ambitious and reaching for the stars.

Squares and triangles

These are common doodles but they're a good sign. They show that you can plan and organize things well. They're also an indication of clear thinking and good direction in life.

Doodle Dandy II

Which of these do you recognize from your doodling?

Animals

You'd be great working to help others – animals or people – and like to protect those close to you.

Flowers

A sign of a loving, caring person who's sensitive and kind to other people.

Swirls

This kind of repeated pattern shows that you're logical and reliable and stick at something once you start doing it.

Faces

If you draw faces all over your notes, it can tell you different things depending upon the kind of face.

Scary faces

If your faces look ugly, dark or scary, it's not a good sign. You should try to trust people more and have confidence in yourself.

Pretty faces

That's more like it! You're confident and good-natured, and look for the best in people. You like to socialize.

Open mouths

If your faces have their mouths open, you may talk too much! Don't talk for the sake of it, or just to hear your own voice.

What Are You Like?

A two-page quiz will never be able to get inside your head and figure out the sort of person you really are. However, it can raise some questions about the real you and how well you know yourself – try this to see what you discover!

1 Which of these describes you?

- [ ] Sociable
- [ ] I like peace and quiet
- [ ] I love to be alone
- [x] Comfortable in groups
- [ ] A leader

2 What are you like with schoolwork?

- [ ] I don't always finish it
- [x] I get it done on time
- [ ] I put it off until the last minute
- [ ] I'm really organized

3 How do you approach new things?

- [ ] Nervously – I'm happier with familiar things
- [ ] I need lots of time to prepare
- [x] I don't plan, I just take it as it comes
- [ ] I don't like making decisions
- [ ] I'm happier doing them as a team

4 How would others describe you?

- [ ] They think I'm rude
- [ ] Annoying – but I enjoy it
- [ ] Helpful
- [x] Very independent
- [ ] Down to earth and straightforward

5 Are you very emotional?

- [ ] Nope, I'm quite cool and calm
- [ ] I certainly let people know if I'm angry
- [x] I get upset if other people are angry or aggressive
- [ ] Yes, I'm easily upset

6 What are your feelings towards other people?

- [ ] I hate upsetting them
- [ ] I'm a sympathetic person
- [ ] I find odd people annoying
- [ ] I'm usually very tolerant

7 Which do you agree with the most?

- [ ] I like to be clear about what others want from me
- [ ] I always keep promises
- [ ] I'm easily embarrassed
- [ ] I'm easy to fool
- [ ] I know exactly what I like and don't like
- [ ] I avoid the company of strangers

Finally, choose five of these words that you are already and three that you would like to be (things that you value in others). They may be the same some of the time!

- [ ] Conventional
- [ ] Organized
- [ ] Creative
- [ ] Humorous
- [ ] Absent-minded
- [ ] Untidy
- [ ] Tactful
- [ ] Assertive
- [ ] Comfortable
- [ ] Competitive
- [ ] Innovative
- [ ] Conscientious
- [ ] Shy
- [ ] Independent
- [ ] Self-controlled
- [ ] Serious
- [ ] Proud
- [ ] Flexible
- [ ] Lazy

What Are You Like? Results

As you've already seen, it's too difficult to analyse everyone with just a few questions like this. However, there are some general characteristics that can be seen in certain answers and not in others.

1 Sociability

Some people can't bear their own company for too long, others can't even think if there are too many people around. There's no right or wrong way to be, you just have to accept that everyone has to spend some time with other people and everyone has to be able to cope alone at times. Read more about this sort of thing on pages 24–27.

2 Organization

What seems like chaos to one person is actually creative and productive to another. You can work your own way (although throughout life, you'll suffer if you can't ever finish a job on time) but don't expect everyone else to work like that.

3 Spontaneity

'Making it up as you go along' is scary for some people. Others just can't bear to be pinned down and have their whole life planned out. Just remember that it's often a matter of confidence – if you believe in yourself, you'll be able to take more risks.

4 Sociability

It's really important that everyone gets along, right? Well, wrong, actually. It's good to have social skills but you don't have to be nice to everyone you ever meet. Trust your judgement and you'll find you don't waste time on people who aren't really your type.

What Are You Like? Results

5 Emotions

There are a huge range of emotions that humans go through. Some people never reach the extremes and they find it easier to control what they're feeling and keep it to themselves. It's good to have highs and lows, but you may find that keeping them to yourself gains you respect from other people.

6 Agreeableness

Most people like to get on together. Some people can't be bothered while others think it's more important than anything else. Don't let yourself be walked all over if you're one of the latter kind of people.

7 Self-knowledge

This whole quiz is about learning more about the real you. It's important to be able to look inside and see what kind of person you're growing up to be. Ticking statements about your own characteristics is a good way to start. It makes you think about how you act and react in different circumstances.

Personality traits

Looking through lists of personality traits is also a good way to see inside. Trying to choose the five words that describe you best can be hard, and sometimes scary. Nobody wants to end up with a list that says they're lazy and gullible and might never have any friends! That's why it's important to list the characteristics you admire in others so that you have some targets to work to. If your lists already match up, then you've already achieved what many grown-ups still hope for – you've shaped yourself into the sort of person you respect, and have taken control of how you live your life. Well done you!

Are You a Meany?

Follow the arrows to find out!

Would you let someone take the blame for something you did? **Y**

Have you ever cheated in your exams? **N** **N**

Do your friends phone you late at night if they need a shoulder to cry on? **Y**

N **Y**

Would you avoid your bessie mate's birthday if she had a karaoke party? **N**

Y

Y

Do you do things for charity? **Y**

Have you ever copied your homework from a friend?

N **N**

Would you lie to get your own way?

N

N

Would you peek at your mate's diary if you got chance? **Y**

Y **N**

Y

Have you ever forgotten your mum's birthday? **Y**

Mean-spirited
You're an out-and-out meany – not with money, but with love and affection for others. You wouldn't go out of your way to help anyone. Learn an early lesson in life – you get out what you put in, so look around and see how you can make the world a better place.

Start Here

Are you good at keeping secrets?

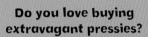

Do you wait for friends to organize sleepovers and invite you?

Would you pay for yourself on a date?

Do you love buying extravagant pressies?

Do you avoid designer clothes because of the price?

Would you do a paper round to earn extra cash for Christmas?

Would you let a date take you to the local caff if it was all he could afford?

Would you spend your last £10 on cheering up a friend who's down?

Do you love spending money, either on yourself or others?

Would you lend a mate your mobile, no problem?

Generous
Hurray for you! You're the kind of person this world needs more of. You don't have to be a fluffety-wuffety all the time, but if you see other people's points of view, and try to help in their rough times, you're spreading a little love and understanding wherever you can. Keep up the good work!

Mean and miserly
Bah, humbug! You might think you're careful with money but others just think you're tight-fisted. Not everyone can splash the cash but it's where you spend your money that counts. Loosen up – both with your attitude and your purse strings – and you'll reap rewards that money can't buy.

Sign Your Name

A graphologist is someone who studies handwriting. But can they tell very much just from the way you sign your name? At school, you might practise your signature as a doodle, but it will probably change when you get older and have to sign cheques and forms. However, there are some things your signature might give away already...

Big signature

If you sign your name in bigger writing than your usual handwriting, it's a sign that you want to be noticed and thought of as important. It's not big-headedness though, just a way of saying 'Don't ignore me.'

Lucy Jones

Illegible signature

If you can't read your signature, especially if it's very complicated and swirly, it's just showing off. Change it so you can read it!

Huggnes

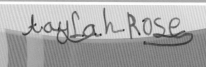

Circle around your name

If you enclose your name in a circle, or a square, it's a sign that you're unhappy with yourself and are closing yourself off from others. Don't be afraid to rely on other people to help cheer you up.

Full stop

A full stop at the end of your signature suggests that you stick to tried and tested ways of doing things. If it's a big, heavy dot, you are an obstinate person!

Lucy Jones.

Underlining

Most underlined names show that you're quite ambitious. The thicker or stronger the line, the more aggressive you are about getting things done. If you put shorter lines across the underline, it means you're keen on cash!

Lucy Jones

Squiggles and squirls

Lots of extra loops under your name mean that you're too keen on what people think of you.

Lucy Jones

Write On

So that's what your signature says – but what can you tell from someone's regular handwriting? Here are a few main clues to look for.

Letter T

Is the bar on the little 't' very long? The writer is usually sarcastic.

> rollerblades. We Met up with Rosie and Hannah
> who had packed a picnic. We sat by the pond ar
> fed our crusts to the ducks.
> There was a fair at the park and we all wen

Spacing

Are the spaces between words bigger than average? That shows the writer would like to be left alone, or feels forced out and lonely.

> ...ven know existed! The posture needed f
> riding will firm your bum and thigh
> strengthen your back and hips. Make sur
> ...go to a reputable riding school

High and low strokes

Look at letters like 'd', 'h' and 'y' that stick up or down from the main writing. If they're very short, making the middle parts of the letters (and letters like 'a' and 'o') seem big in comparison, it's not a good sign! It shows immature writing, and someone who's still forming ideas and wanting to be important.

> ey laugh or make nasty comments d
> ut off. They could be trying to cover u
> wn shyness. Try again when they're o
> wn. If they're rude again, it's probabl
> find someone else. There's so much

Large handwriting

'Normal' handwriting size is usually about 3 mm for a letter 'o', and an extra 3 mm for the high and low parts of a 'd' or 'y'. If the writing is bigger than that, it's sometimes a sign of someone pretending to be more confident than they really are. Often, though, it shows an extrovert and sociable personality.

Small handwriting

Anything under this 'normal' size is a sign that the writer is more introverted and less confident. Often it shows that they're quite good at school subjects and exams, too.

Heavy, thick writing

If it looks like the person has been pressing on the paper really hard, it can show that they're stressed or under pressure. If they always write like that, it's a sign they don't like being criticised.

Read on for more tell-tale signs in your schoolbooks...

Write On II

Sloping writing

Lots of people's writing slopes forwards or backwards. Sometimes this is misleading – if the writer is left-handed it's likely to slope backwards because of the way they position their paper. However, if that's not the case...

Backwards sloping writing shows that the writer tries to be true to themself before pleasing others. They may be quite reserved.

-ronment, politics, animal right
-ght feel that you can't make a
-ou approach it properly. Peop

Forwards slope is a sign that the person wants to be involved with others. It's usually a positive thing, showing affection or sociable personalities. If it's too far sloping it can be bad, though, and show impatience and forgetfulness.

Which of these would be yo
-ery worst nightmare? Whic
-them could you avoid? W

Fat versus thin

Look at the three different sections of the letters – the middle section (like a letter 'o'), plus the tops of high letters ('d' and 'h') and bottoms of low letters ('y' and 'g'). Are any of them more rounded and full or 'fat' than the other sections? Here's what it could tell you:

Full middle section is the sign of an individualist who's good-tempered, warm-hearted and likes a certain amount of routine in their life.

Full upper section indicates a good imagination and creative mind. If it's too full and fat, it can mean you're a daydreamer or aren't good at concentrating.

Full lower section shows the writer may be money-minded, with a strong emphasis on the physical side of life (such as a sporty person), too.

Fun Time

Have you ever read interviews with your favourite pop and movie stars, and wished you were famous enough to be asked them too? Well, here's your chance! Write in your own answers or use the questions to interview your friends and have a laugh about your decisions.

1 What's your most embarrassing moment ever?

3 If you were a biscuit, what kind would you be?

4 Can you cook pancakes?

2 What's your favourite colour and how does it make you feel?

5 What's your favourite school subject?

6 What tunes are you listening to these days?

7 Who would you like to play the part of you if a film of your life was made?

8 Where's your favourite holiday destination?

9 What's your worst-ever fashion mistake?

10 What song would you sing if you made an appearance on 'pop idol'?

11 Have you ever dreamt about fancying someone who's not that fanciable?

12 What's in your coat pockets?

13 Which animal are you most like and why?

14 Who would you most like to meet, living or dead?

15 Which of the Scooby Doo gang is most like you?

Now try these quick-fire choices:

Trainers or shoes?

Boxers or pants?

Cereal or toast?

Pyjamas or nothing?

JK Rowling or Philip Pullman?

Shopping or chatting?

TV or gaming?

Simon Cowell or Louis Walsh?

Jeans or combats?

Silver or gold?

Go Getters

How ambitious are you? Follow the arrows and see where you end up on the scale!

Start Here

Are you looking forward to leaving school?

Do you enjoy going to parties?

Do you agree that the best things in life are free?

Do you already have an idea what you want?

Would you risk a friendship over someone you fancy?

Do you always play to win?

Are you proud of the jobs your family do?

Do you like to captain your team?

Have you got lots of famous heroes/heroines?

N **N** **Y** **Y** **N** **N** **N** **Y** **N** **Y** **Y** **Y** **N** **Y** **N** **N** **Y**

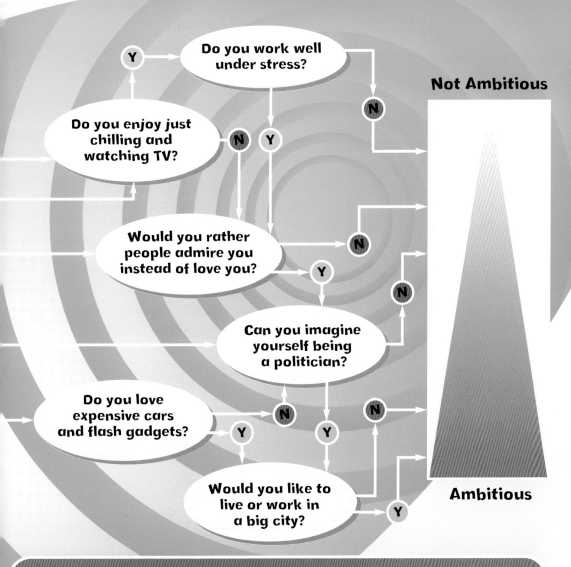

Do you work well under stress? Y N

Not Ambitious

Do you enjoy just chilling and watching TV? N Y

Would you rather people admire you instead of love you? N Y

Can you imagine yourself being a politician? N

Do you love expensive cars and flash gadgets? N Y

Would you like to live or work in a big city? Y

Ambitious

If you're this high on the scale, you're not ambitious. You like your creature comforts and don't want to push yourself too hard. If your answers led you further down, it shows that you could achieve good things if you try. Don't hold yourself back. The further down the scale you are, the more ambition you have. You're not afraid to go for what you want. If you're at the bottom, you're heading for the cut-throat world of business. It's your choice whether you want power or money — but keep in touch with your caring side as you work towards your goals.

Animal Magic

Choose your three favourite animals from these pages and then turn over to see what each one says about you.

Eagle

Horse

Bear

Rabbit

Frog

Lion

Owl

Squirrel

Giraffe

Monkey

Dolphin

Wolf

67

Animal Magic Results

Eagle
You have the ability to balance power and elegance and are tuned in to your spiritual side. You're wise and brave and you can see underneath the surface of things to find out what's really going on.

Horse
You love your friends, travelling and your freedom. You're loyal and co-operative and good at communicating.

Rabbit
Seize the day! That's your motto – you live life to the full and take all the opportunities it gives. You're gentle and considerate to others as well as yourself.

Bear
You're quite dreamy and other-worldly and sometimes not bothered about socializing. You know yourself well as you spend a long time pondering over your own qualities and how to interact with others.

Frog
You're a very basic, down to earth person who loves to study and increase your knowledge or understanding of life.

Owl
Caring and visionary, you'd make a great teacher or therapist because you're good at listening and having insight into other people's problems. You're good at keeping secrets, too.

Lion

Strong and brave, you're full of energy and can quite easily relax and get rid of stress through exercise. You can be a bit selfish sometimes but are very loyal to your family.

Wolf

You're intelligent but can also trust your instincts. You love change, although you stay true to your oldest friends.

Giraffe

You're intuitive and good at communicating. Just like your chosen animal, you can see and achieve things that are out of reach for ordinary people. You're also able to rise above any rabble with your dignity intact.

Dolphin

You love harmony and balance – yoga would be a great hobby for you. Your emotions build up and you need to release them calmly.

Squirrel

Get busy and stay busy – hard work reaps its rewards. You're quite a chatterbox, but you're clever and resourceful, and good at planning ahead.

Monkey

Your health is important to you, but it's important to learn not to overdo things – eating, socializing or exercising. You're looking for success in your life, without treading on others to get it.

Can You Stand On Your Own Two Feet?

1 Which of these describes you on holiday?
- a. I stick with my family and do what they're doing each day ☐
- b. I like to join the kids' club and see what activities they have ☐
- c. I'm happiest on my own, exploring or just swimming and sunbathing ☐

2 Where do you get your spending money from?
- a. I work at the weekends – I've even started to enjoy it ☐
- b. I get pocket money but get extra from my grandparents ☐
- c. I do a paper round and babysit sometimes ☐

3 How do you revise for exams?
- a. I shut myself in the library and swot up ☐
- b. I get together with my friends and swap notes ☐
- c. I sometimes ask my mum to test me on what I've learnt ☐

4 You've arranged to see a film, but your friends let you down. What do you do?
- a. Wait until next week to see it, your friends will be free then ☐
- b. Find someone else to go to the cinema with you to see it ☐
- c. Wait until it's out on DVD, you can watch it anytime then ☐

5 You want to go into town but your mum doesn't like the idea. How do you get round her?
- a. Get your friends to talk to her ☐
- b. Don't go ☐
- c. Persuade your mum with the offer of cleaning the house the whole of next week ☐

6 You're buying new boots for the winter. How do you decide what to spend your money on?
- a. You saw a fab pair in town, so you'll just buy those ☐
- b. You've seen a few pairs in your catalogue, so you'll show your friends for their opinion ☐
- c. Your friends all buy the latest style, so you get those, too ☐

7 How do you wire a plug?
- a. Brown wire is live, blue is neutral, there might be a third wire for earth ☐
- b. Blue wire is live, brown wire is neutral, the other one is earth ☐
- c. I have absolutely no idea ☐

8 How long does it take to boil an egg?
- a. don't know, I've never cooked one ☐
- b. About five minutes ☐
- c. Three or four minutes for soft boiled, about ten for hard boiled eggs ☐

9 You've been invited to a party but no one will be home to give you a lift. What do you do?
- a. Apologise, but you won't be able to go to the party ☐
- b. Ask if anyone else who's going can pick you up on the way ☐
- c. Find out the times of buses that will get you there ☐

10 Your parents are going out on Saturday night. What have you got planned?
- a. A cool night with popcorn and chocolate and only you in charge of the remote control ☐
- b. Your friends are coming for a sleepover ☐
- c. You're going to stay at your best friend's house for the night ☐

Answers

Questions 1 a=1 b=2 c=3	Questions 6 a=3 b=2 c=1
Questions 2 a=3 b=1 c=2	Questions 7 a=3 b=2 c=1
Questions 3 a=3 b=1 c=2	Questions 8 a=1 b=2 c=3
Questions 4 a=2 b=3 c=1	Questions 9 a=1 b=2 c=3
Questions 5 a=1 b=2 c=3	Questions 10 a=3 b=2 c=1

Less than 15

If you scored less than 15 you're definitely not yet a woman, as Britney would say. You need to learn a few more life lessons and help yourself more than you do. It's great doing things with friends, but you should be confident enough to go it alone

16–24

If you scored between 16 and 24 you're starting to make your own way in the world. You know how to handle things and get to places under your own steam, but you still prefer to have company when you're out and about.

More than 25

If you scored more than 25 you're one of Destiny's Child's 'Independent Women'. Not only do you like your own company, you get more done on your own sometimes. You'd be good to have around in an emergency. Can you fix it? Yes, you probably can!

Are You a Potential Genius?

Not many people are remembered as geniuses. The few who are have certain things in common – perhaps you're cast in the same mould? Add up your scores using the table on the next page.

1 Someone is saying something you really don't agree with. Do you speak out?
- a. I'd rather have a quiet life ☐
- b. Possibly, it depends who else was there ☐
- c. Yep! I'm entitled to my say! ☐

2 Which of these do you enjoy the most?
- a. Watching TV ☐
- b. Reading ☐
- c. Writing ☐

3 What's the best way for you to get your studying done?
- a. With a steady buzz of noise in the background ☐
- b. In total silence ☐
- c. It doesn't matter, you lose yourself in what you're doing ☐

4 What kind of exams do you prefer?
- a. Essay answers ☐
- b. Multiple-choice answers ☐
- c. Comprehension questions where the answers are from the exam question itself ☐

5 Someone pushes into the lunch queue. What do you do?
- a. Cough politely and say sorry, but you were there first ☐
- b. Just let them do it, who cares? ☐
- c. Make a big deal of it at top volume until you embarrass them into moving back ☐

6 Do you play chess?
- a. No – never understood it ☐
- b. Well, ye-es, but not often and not that well ☐
- c. Yeah, it's a fab game ☐

7 Which of these describes you?
- a. You like to follow someone else's tried and tested method ☐
- b. You love experimenting with new ways ☐
- c. Whatever – you're so laid back you'll go along with either way ☐

8 Do you sneak a look at your Christmas presents?
- a. What's the point? ☐
- b. Well, it has been known... ☐
- c. Who doesn't? ☐

9 Do you gaze at your blank notebook/computer screen for ages before you get inspiration with your work?

a. Yeah, all the time. Writer's block, isn't it? ☐

b. No, I can't remember doing that, thank goodness. ☐

c. Well, I guess I get stuck sometimes like most people ☐

10 Do you like team sports?

a. Aaaargh, no! Hate them! ☐

b. They're okay as sports go ☐

c. They're definitely my favourite way to do exercise ☐

11 Do you enjoy maths?

a. No, it's one of my worst, most boring subjects ever ☐

b. Luvvit – it's really interesting when you get to grips with it ☐

c. I don't mind it – it's more useful than some other subjects ☐

12 Does your mind keep working when you sleep, giving you new ideas in your dreams?

a. Er – no. Weird! ☐

b. I guess, sometimes ☐

c. Cool, yeah, it's amazing when that happens ☐

13 Do you like going to parties?

a. I'd rather read or watch TV ☐

b. They're okay, as long as my friends are all going ☐

c. Party – where? Hand me my house keys, I'm there already! ☐

14 Do you sneak food from the kitchen while dinner is being prepared?

a. I'd rather wait for the meal ☐

b. Yeah! Everyone does, right? ☐

c. Sometimes I just can't resist ☐

15 Are you easily put off if others criticize what you're doing?

a. Yup – it's obviously rubbish so why waste more time on it? ☐

b. Nope – what do they know? ☐

c. Maybe, it depends what I'm doing and who sees it ☐

16 Do you rev people up to make them do stuff they don't think they want to do?

a. Definitely, some people are just rubbish at getting started ☐

b. Yes, sometimes I'm enthusiastic enough to get others involved ☐

c. No – they'd probably end up hating me for making them do it ☐

17 Would you stay up all night to do extra work on a project?

a. No way! ☐

b. I guess, if I didn't have other stuff going on that would suffer ☐

c. For sure – sometimes it's better to get things finished ☐

18 Do you sometimes wish you'd done more on your homework before you hand it in?

a. No, you usually get the amount about right ☐

b. No, there's better things to do ☐

c. Sometimes you're not satisfied with what you produced ☐

19 Do you have many hobbies?

a. Lots ☐

b. A few that you concentrate on ☐

c. One that takes all of your time ☐

20 Do you get frustrated because others don't get your ideas?

a. Yes, I struggle to make all of my thoughts understood ☐

b. No, I'm good at explaining ☐

c. No, everyone gets my ideas ☐

Are You a Potential Genius? Results

Tick your answers and add up the scores.

Question 1	a=0	b=5	c=10		Question 11	a=0	b=10	c=5
Question 2	a=0	b=5	c=10		Question 12	a=0	b=5	c=10
Question 3	a=5	b=0	c=10		Question 13	a=10	b=5	c=0
Question 4	a=10	b=0	c=5		Question 14	a=10	b=0	c=5
Question 5	a=5	b=0	c=10		Question 15	a=0	b=10	c=5
Question 6	a=0	b=5	c=10		Question 16	a=10	b=5	c=0
Question 7	a=5	b=10	c=0		Question 17	a=0	b=5	c=10
Question 8	a=10	b=5	c=0		Question 18	a=5	b=0	c=10
Question 9	a=0	b=10	c=5		Question 19	a=0	b=5	c=10
Question 10	a=10	b=5	c=0		Question 20	a=10	b=5	c=0

0–50

You won't be remembered as a genius. Your strengths lie in other areas – but that's not bad. You're a practical person who can programme the DVD, make your own meals and generally live a regular life. You should have lots of friends and be well-liked.

55–150

Sorry, no geniuses here. You're intelligent and well-rounded but you lack some ambition and drive that a genius needs. You're just too nice and spend more time working on your relationships with friends and family than working on a world-changing theory.

155–200

If your generation is hiding a genius, this group is where we should look. You have the makings of someone who's obsessive about what they do, full of ideas and hooked on their subject. Read on to find out what makes a genius and do the quick test to see if you've got the brain power to match your will power!

BRAIN POWER TEST

Are you brainy enough to be a genius? Try these five questions – you've only got five minutes to do them all – and geniuses need to get five out of five!

1. Which of these is the odd one out?

   A   N   E   F   H

2. 150 people enter a pop star competition. 70 percent of entrants are chosen for the second round, two-thirds of those lucky ones make it to the third round and 3 out of 14 get kicked out in the last qualifying round. How many of the original entrants make it to the TV finals?

3. A is to B as C is to...?

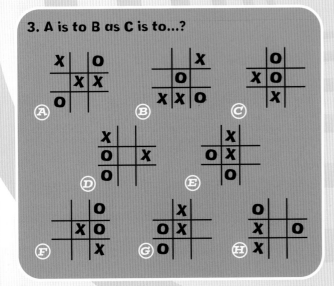

4. What comes next in this number sequence?

   84, 80, 72, 60, ?

5. How long will 72 sausages last if 6 people each eat 2 sausages every 3 minutes?

2. 55   3. D   4. 44 (-4, -8, -12, -16)   5. 18 minutes
1. E – all the others are made up of just 3 straight lines.

ANSWERS

All Fingers and Thumbs

Do you wear jewellery on our hands? What do you so with your thumbs when you're holding hands? Your digits can reveal or sorts of things – check out the hands of everyone you meet!

Thumb

It used to be rare to see people wearing rings here, so it was the sign of a very individual person. Nowadays, thumb rings are trendy so it's not such a bold statement. The thumb is the part of your hand representing willpower, so wearing a ring is restricting that side of yourself.

The thumb is separate from the fingers, and the more you hold it away from them, the more independent you want to be. If you notice someone's thumbs before the rest of their hand, it's a sign that they're free-thinking and don't like to be made to conform.

Using your thumb to cover someone else's fingers as you hold hands shows that you want to make them think like you. If their hand is smothered by your thumb, you should lighten up and allow them some space to do their own thing.

Index finger

This is the finger next to your thumb. It's no coincidence that it's your pointing finger, as it's your 'authority' finger. From an early age, children learn to wag it when they're telling you off, or trying to stop you from saying something.

Watch how people use this finger. Do they put it to their lips, trying to hold back what they say?

Do they sit with both index fingers on the sides of their head, trying to organize their thoughts? If they drink with this finger around their cup, using the other fingers to hold the cup in place, watch out! They want to take charge.

If you wear a ring on your index finger, you're showing that you restrict your own authority. You're also 'prettifying' the one finger that commands respect from other people. Are you more concerned with looking good than making people listen to your point of view?

All Fingers and Thumbs II

Middle finger

Look at your outstretched hand. This finger is usually the longest, often the straightest and is dead centre. It sums you up as an individual.

Wearing a ring on this finger suggests that you're not sure of where you stand. You want to draw attention to yourself sometimes, but you're prepared to wear jewellery to disguise what you really are. Quite often, this finger is used to wear big, dramatic rings that reach to the knuckle. You're hiding your true self behind a bold statement – or you're very confident of who you are and are showing off to the world.

Ring finger

This is called the ring finger because it's where an engagement or wedding ring is worn. As such, it shows your affections and artistic, creative side. Many people can't move it properly without moving one of the fingers next to it. Are you independent, or do you like to be linked to others?

Because this finger shows your creativity, it's important to see what kind of jewellery is worn on it. Is it a plain wedding band, or a huge glittery jewel? Quite often, extravagant jewellery is a sign of an uncreative person – someone who's had to use another person's imagination and design to decorate their own hand.

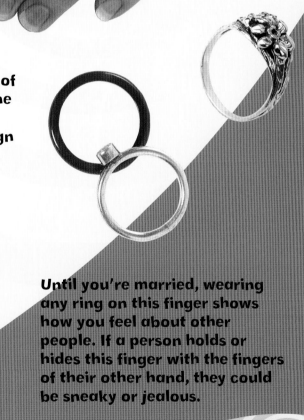

Until you're married, wearing any ring on this finger shows how you feel about other people. If a person holds or hides this finger with the fingers of their other hand, they could be sneaky or jealous.

All Fingers and Thumbs III

Little finger

This is your cutest finger, and usually your weakest one. It's the furthest one from your thumb (representing your independent self) so it's linked to your relationships. Mostly, it's the one that points to the outside world and other people.

Wearing a ring on this finger shows that you're unsure of your relationships. You might find it difficult to make friends, or to say what you're really thinking. You're unsure about how other people view you, so you try to disguise or restrict the finger with jewellery.

If a person holds their little finger separate from their other fingers (for example, when they're drinking) they're showing off, asserting their individuality or showing themselves to be friendly and open.

What else can you tell from a person's hands? Make sure you study your own and look after them to give the right impression to other people.

Biting nails

This is the most obvious sign that a person is nervous or stressed. Stop biting yours NOW! Even if you are nervous, it's better not to give the game away before you've even spoken. If people think you're a little bit confident, they'll treat you with more respect.

Manicured nails

If you take the time to clean, file and paint your nails, it shows the outside world that you care. Carefully looked-after nails don't even have to be painted to show that you take pride in doing things properly.

Intertwined fingers

If two people hold hands with fingers linked, it's a sign of a balanced relationship. Neither is trying to take over the other.

Friends and Family

How do you feel about your life and the people closest to you? Take this fun test to find out! Put these animals in order of preference (write down your favourite one at the top down to your least fave at the bottom).

Cow

Horse

Sheep

Pig

Tiger

1. Horses
2. Tigers
3. Sheeps
4. Pigs
5. Cows

Now look at the pictures below for a minute. On the dotted lines write just ONE word to describe each one.

1

2

3

4

5

1. Dogs
2. Cat
3. Ocean
4. Coffee
5. Rats

Who do these colours remind you of? Write a different name under each colour – try to think of people close to you, not famous people or people you fancy and haven't really met.

Theo   Kacey   MumDad   Erin M   Alexander

Now let's look at what it all means...

Horse
If you put **HORSE** at the top of the list, your family is the most important thing to you. You treasure them and look to them for advice and an idea of what you want to be like yourself.

Pig
If you chose **PIG** for your first item you're ruled by money. It might be that you haven't any money, so it's more important to you than it is to others. Try not to seem greedy or tight.

Sheep
People who put **SHEEP** value love above everything else. It's important for you to be loved and to have people who you shower you with love. You will be good at spotting that special person.

Cow
The position of the **COW** shows how important a career is. If it's high up, you want to do well at school and have a job that makes you fulfilled. If it's lower down, you're not be as bothered.

Tiger
If **TIGER** was top of your list, you're a proud person who wants to do well and it's important that other people respect you. Try not to be too proud, as you might scare off friends.

Words for each picture describe how you feel about these people and things:
DOG → Yourself
CAT → Your loved ones
RAT → Your enemies
COFFEE → Your relationships with others
SEA → Your own life

And finally, the names you wrote down are important because:
Yellow → this is a person you will always remember
Orange → a proper, true friend to you
Red → someone you really love
White → someone really like you, you both have lots in common
Green → someone who will always be there when you need them

83

Job Centre

Have you thought about what job you'd like to do? The subjects you choose for **GCSEs** will help to structure your career path. Use this personality list, and the knowledge you've gained about yourself from this book, to see what career might suit you.

Section 1
Which of these is your favourite area?
- **W**ords
- **A**rt
- **P**ractical studies
- **E**xperimenting
- **O**rganizing
- **B**usiness
- **S**ocial

Section 2
Which word in each pair best describes your personality?
- **F**actual
- **I**maginative
- **S**pontaneous
- **D**eliberate
- **A**ssertive
- **P**assive
- **G**roup
- **S**olitary

Section 3
Which is your first, second and third strongest area?
1st 2nd 3rd
- ☐ ☐ ☐ **O**dd one out puzzles
- ☐ ☐ ☐ **N**umber puzzles
- ☐ ☐ ☐ **L**ogic puzzles
- ☐ ☐ ☐ **P**icture matching puzzles
- ☐ ☐ ☐ **3-D** puzzles
- ☐ ☐ ☐ **C**odes and ciphers
- ☐ ☐ ☐ **V**ocabulary tests
- ☐ ☐ ☐ **M**aths tests

Transfer your ticks to the boxes below, ticking one in the first column, four in the second column, and three in the last. Now look at the tables on the next pages for a job that you might like. If several ticks are the same as yours, you have a good match.

My results	Section 1							Section 2								Section 3							
	W	A	P	E	O	B	S	F	I	Sp	D	A	P	G	S	O	N	L	P	3d	C	V	M
Accountant				✓	✓			✓		✓	✓							✓			✓		✓
Actor	✓	✓						✓	✓										✓			✓	
Advertising	✓		✓									✓	✓			✓	✓	✓			✓		
Airline cabin crew		✓	✓				✓	✓	✓			✓	✓										
Ambulance crew			✓				✓	✓			✓		✓										
Architect			✓								✓	✓	✓		✓	✓	✓		✓	✓		✓	
Armed forces				✓		✓	✓	✓				✓		✓		✓	✓					✓	
Artist			✓								✓			✓			✓						
Art dealer			✓			✓					✓	✓											
Astronaut		✓	✓					✓			✓	✓				✓	✓					✓	✓
Baker			✓								✓		✓	✓									
Bank manager				✓	✓			✓			✓	✓		✓				✓			✓	✓	
Beautician			✓				✓	✓	✓				✓					✓					
Bilingual secretary	✓										✓		✓		✓			✓			✓	✓	
Biologist				✓				✓				✓		✓		✓	✓						
Bookseller						✓						✓					✓						
Botanist				✓							✓		✓	✓	✓	✓							
Careers advisor						✓						✓											
Carpenter		✓									✓		✓	✓						✓			
Cartoonist		✓						✓			✓	✓		✓						✓			
Caterer		✓			✓				✓			✓		✓						✓			
Chemist				✓				✓				✓		✓		✓	✓				✓		
Child care worker						✓						✓	✓										
Chiropodist				✓			✓	✓				✓		✓	✓	✓					✓		
Civil engineer		✓	✓					✓				✓						✓		✓			✓
Civil servant						✓		✓				✓				✓	✓				✓	✓	✓
Computer game designer			✓					✓	✓			✓		✓		✓				✓	✓	✓	
Copywriter	✓							✓						✓			✓					✓	

85

Job Centre II

My results

My results	Section 1							Section 2								Section 3							
	W	A	P	E	O	B	S	F	I	Sp	D	A	P	G	S	O	N	L	P	3d	C	V	M
Counsellor							✓	✓	✓			✓	✓										
Curator	✓	✓							✓		✓		✓		✓			✓	✓				
Dancer		✓						✓	✓														
Decorator		✓							✓				✓					✓					
Dentist				✓			✓	✓			✓	✓				✓	✓	✓	✓				
Designer		✓						✓	✓					✓				✓					
DJ		✓							✓	✓	✓												
Doctor				✓		✓						✓		✓		✓	✓				✓	✓	
Ecologist		✓							✓		✓	✓				✓							
Editor	✓								✓		✓	✓							✓			✓	✓
Electrical engineer		✓	✓					✓			✓							✓		✓			
Estate agent						✓	✓				✓		✓										✓
Farmer		✓			✓									✓				✓					
Fashion designer		✓							✓	✓		✓						✓					
Firefighter		✓									✓			✓				✓					
Forensic scientist				✓				✓			✓	✓			✓	✓	✓				✓		
Geologist				✓				✓			✓	✓		✓		✓		✓					
Hairdresser		✓					✓	✓	✓					✓				✓					
Illustrator		✓							✓		✓			✓				✓					
Interpreter	✓							✓	✓			✓		✓			✓						
Journalist	✓							✓	✓	✓									✓			✓	
Judge	✓									✓	✓			✓					✓			✓	
Lab technician				✓				✓			✓			✓		✓			✓				
Lawyer	✓								✓	✓									✓			✓	✓
Librarian	✓			✓	✓			✓			✓	✓		✓	✓						✓	✓	
Market researcher				✓	✓			✓			✓	✓							✓		✓		
Mechanic				✓				✓			✓	✓		✓							✓		

My results

	Section 1							Section 2								Section 3							
	W	A	P	E	O	B	S	F	I	Sp	D	A	P	G	S	O	N	L	P	3d	C	V	M
Midwife				✓			✓	✓		✓	✓		✓			✓							
Nanny							✓	✓	✓		✓												
Nurse				✓			✓	✓		✓			✓	✓		✓							
Occupational therapist	✓	✓					✓	✓		✓	✓		✓								✓	✓	
Optician				✓				✓			✓		✓	✓		✓						✓	
Personal trainer							✓			✓			✓	✓									
Pharmacist				✓		✓		✓			✓	✓				✓					✓		
Photographer	✓							✓	✓		✓			✓					✓				
Physiotherapist	✓						✓	✓	✓		✓		✓	✓		✓			✓				
Pilot		✓		✓				✓			✓		✓	✓		✓		✓	✓			✓	
Police officer				✓			✓				✓		✓							✓			
Politician						✓	✓				✓		✓	✓			✓						
Postman/woman				✓							✓		✓		✓								
Prison officer				✓			✓	✓			✓												
Producer	✓				✓	✓		✓			✓		✓	✓		✓		✓			✓		
Programmer					✓	✓		✓			✓		✓	✓		✓		✓	✓	✓			
Psychiatrist	✓			✓				✓			✓		✓	✓		✓	✓				✓		
Psychologist				✓									✓		✓	✓	✓	✓					
Quantity surveyor		✓						✓			✓				✓	✓	✓		✓	✓		✓	
Sales person							✓			✓	✓												✓
Secretary	✓	✓						✓			✓		✓								✓		✓
Social worker							✓	✓			✓		✓										
Speech therapist							✓	✓	✓				✓		✓	✓							
Stockbroker					✓	✓		✓			✓		✓					✓					✓
Surgeon				✓				✓			✓		✓		✓	✓	✓		✓	✓			
Surveyor		✓		✓				✓			✓		✓			✓		✓					
Systems analyst					✓	✓		✓		✓						✓		✓		✓			
Teacher							✓						✓	✓		✓	✓	✓					
Travel agent		✓		✓				✓	✓												✓		
Vet		✓	✓					✓			✓					✓	✓		✓	✓			
Youth worker							✓						✓	✓									
Zoo keeper	✓			✓				✓						✓				✓					

Half-full or Half-empty?

How optimistic are you? Do you always look on the bright side of life, or permanently see doom and gloom ahead? Tick true or false for each statement, then count up to see which description fits you the best.

1 I'd never ask someone out – they'd probably say no

☐ True ☐ False

2 People on the street sometimes call out, "Cheer up, it might never happen!" to me

☐ True ☐ False

3 If my aunt or uncle won the lottery, they wouldn't share the money with us

☐ True ☐ False

4 I get scared going on a plane in case it crashes

☐ True ☐ False

5 When I'm old enough, I won't vote as politicians are liars

☐ True ☐ False

6 My favourite flavour of ice cream is always the one to sell out first

☐ True ☐ False

7 I don't want a pet because they're hard work for little reward

☐ True ☐ False

8 If I wake up after a bad dream, I'm scared to fall asleep again in case it comes back

☐ True ☐ False

9 I try to buy trendy clothes but leave it too late so they're out of fashion

☐ True ☐ False

10 I always carry my bag in front of me in case someone tries to steal from it

☐ True ☐ False

11 My little brother/sister is going to grow up to be much cleverer than me

☐ True ☐ False

12 I stick with the 'in-crowd' at school so I'm less likely to be bullied

☐ True ☐ False

Answers

Mostly true

You do have a gloomy outlook, don't you? Don't be a moaning Minnie – life is there for the living, so try to make the most of every opportunity. Sometimes you feel that you're just being realistic, when everyone else is seeing the world through rose-tinted glasses. Bear in mind there's a saying that you make your own luck. If you look for the best in things, the best things tend to happen. So stick your chin in the air, throw your shoulders back and be confident about deserving the good things in life.

Mostly false

That's more like it! You seem to be a cheerful type who bounces back when life knocks you down. It's a great attitude to have and will serve you well in life. People who look on the bright side seem to ride over the top of bad fortune and leave it trailing behind. Just one word of warning – if you permanently have a grin on your face, you might be the sort of person your friends avoid if they need support or sympathy. Show a bit of compassion and understanding, and they'll lean on you when they're going through a black patch.

Boys, Boys, Boys!

What kind of guy is your Mr Right?
Follow the pink arrows for True and the blue arrows for False.

You can tell a lot about a boy from his trainers

F

I like the idea of a mysterious boyfriend

F — I'm keep-fit crazy

T

F

T

I'm super spontaneous

T

T

I'm not looking for money, I'm looking for laughs

F

T

I'm up with the girls and ready for fun

F

Hmm, hard to get – I'm intrigued

T

I like 'em scruffy!

F

T

T

I ♥ my teddy!

F

T

T

F

Crowds are cool, especially if it's a whole footie team!

F

F

T

T

I always look on the bright side

F

T

The specky boys at school are kind of cute, you know!

F

Chunky hunky!
If boys were ice cream, they'd be your scoop! You like the outdoors type, preferably with a good bod, and you're not afraid of having a laugh with the boys. Don't expect lazy Sundays though!

Start

I feel ready to fall in love — F / T

I always fall for the cheeky tricksters

Life's a bit boring – my dream world is miles better

I need a hero in my life

Close out the world, I'm reading my book

I want someone older and mature

Life is dull unless you seize the day

I want to party, now and forever!

I'm a no-nonsense, ass-kicking kinda girl, raring to go

Bored, bored, bored – never!

People say I talk a lot

Nights in with friends and a movie can be really cool

I'm thoughtful about my future

Sweet as chocolate!
Ahh! You're attracted to dreamy types who'll gaze into your eyes and hold your hand. If poetry is your ideal, then get your head out of the clouds for a while and focus on the reality of fancying someone!

Tutti frutti!
Variety is the spice of life and you're want a guy who's game for adventure. He may be a skater boy but life's not dull with him around. Put your hair up, sling on your running shoes and have fun!

Fit or Not?

Follow this fun flow chart to find out what kind of a fitness gal you really are!

catching up on the goss

sit and chill

During school breaks, I like to...

head outside

One of my main hobbies is...

watching TV

When I'm angry, I tend to...

playing on the computer

I can't stand it when...

keep it all inside until I burst

My best friends think I'm...

it rains and I'm stuck in

it's too hot and saps my energy

lovely just the way I am

a good listener

When I'm with my family...

mad and unpredictable

I can't wait to be with my friends

Couch potato
You seem to do a lot of talking, TV-watching and relaxing. Something must change or you'll end up lazy and overweight. Find a gym that lets you watch TV while you jog.

Runner bean
You're full of energy! You lead a hectic lifestyle that keeps you active. Try channelling some energy into a sport. It might help you to concentrate and focus a bit more.

Start

On a night out, my fave thing is...

dancing all night

During sports lessons, I'd be picked early because...

I'm really good

I'm really popular

join all the clubs

take it out on those around me

Saturdays are great for...

When I'm on holiday, I...

going shopping

going to netball/judo/soccer

catching up on watching soaps

try all the sports available

I use my mobile most for...

we love sitting and talking a lot

phoning home for a lift

texting friends

Peas in a pod
Life's one big party! You're happiest with friends. Think how fun it would be to get your friends together and start a team. Burn off energy whilst working your bod!

Keeny beanie
You already know that you like sports! It's great to be so fit and healthy, but make sure you spend time with friends. Get them to play frisbee or grab some rollerblades!

Conclusion

Well, then! What have you learnt about yourself and all the other people you've studied? Have you made any scientific inroads? Perhaps you've developed great new theories linking left-handedness to a love of pizza and dolphins?!

Keep a record

If you really are interested in scientific study, of psychology or any other area, it's a good idea to start noting down your findings for future reference. Keep a notebook with the quiz scores and personality types of everyone you tested. Look at the way the quizzes are written, and try to make up your own revealing personality tests or experiments.

What are you like?

It's important when you study people closely to use your findings wisely. Imagine that you've done all the tests yourself and discovered some things you hadn't realized about yourself. You may have thought you were outgoing, but you turned out to be quite introverted. You may now realize that you're not ready to be independent, or that you're less ambitious or more mean than you thought.

Don't worry!

Don't panic! These tests, apart from being lighthearted and fun, can't make you be a particular sort of person. All they do is highlight some of your features. They can also show you different ways of approaching life. If you don't like what you read about yourself, think about how you could change that.

Have some fun!

Don't be afraid to try on new personalities, just the same as you try on new clothes. If you'd rather be more outgoing, or more organized, or more thoughtful – you can be. Turn your weak points into your strongest points, and make the most of things that are individual about you.

So go on – take a few personalities into the cubicle, and try them on for size!

Aknowledgements

The publishers wish to thank the following artists who have contributed to this book:
Louisa Leitao, Helen Parsley

The publishers wish to thank the following photographer and models who contributed to this book:
Photographer: Trevor Clifford
Models: Amy Adams, Rose Arkell, Becky Evans, Miriam Evans Laura Faulder, Louisa Leitao, Alice Mcghee, Liberty Newton Laura Nundram, Ashleigh Smith, Laura Smith, Maria Tennant

All other photographs are from:
Hemera, Photodisc